rhythm & Blues

Book Two

by WESLEY SCHAUM

Foreword

Contemporary sounds and syncopated tempos heard on today's radio and TV provide fascinating educational material as well as valuable technical studies. This collection of fun-to-learn solos is based on popular music both past and present, including ragtime, jazz, blues, boogie-woogie as well as many of the latest styles.

Besides teaching rhythms, these compositions provide additional experience with a variety of key signatures, time signatures, phrase groups, touches, fingerings and musical terms. This book is designed for teen-agers and pre-teens who will especially enjoy this type of music.

Index

TITLE	PAGE	TITLE	PAGE
BIG BLAST	23	JALOPY CAT	4
CHIP DIP	17	JUKE BOX BLUES	22
COME ALIVE!	6	LIVELY ONE	2
DIME-A-DOZEN	20	RAMBLIN'	7
ELEPHANT TWIST, THE	11	ROLLIN' RHYTHM	12
GET SMART	14	RUNAROUND	21
GET UP AND GO-GO	16	THINK YOUNG	10
GIANT BURGER BLUES	8	27 FLAVORS BLUES	18
HUSH PUPPY BLUES	3	SHE-WON'T-LISTEN BLUES	13

SCHAUM PUBLICATIONS, INC.
2018 E. North Ave.   Milwaukee, Wis. 53202

©Copyright 1966 by Schaum Publications, Inc., Milwaukee, Wisconsin
International Copyright Secured   All Rights Reserved
Printed in U.S.A.

WARNING — The reproduction of any part of this publication without prior written consent of Schaum Publications, Inc. is prohibited by U.S. Copyright Law and is subject to penalty. This prohibition extends to mimeograph, Xerox and any other method of copying or printing and to magnetic tape. Showing by any projector (slide, filmstrip, acetate, overhead, opaque, etc.) and by video tape is also illegal. All persons are cautioned and urged to observe this law.

Lively One

Hush Puppy Blues

DIRECTIONS: This piece is very effective when the eighth notes are performed with an uneven rhythm:

Jalopy Cat

Come Alive!

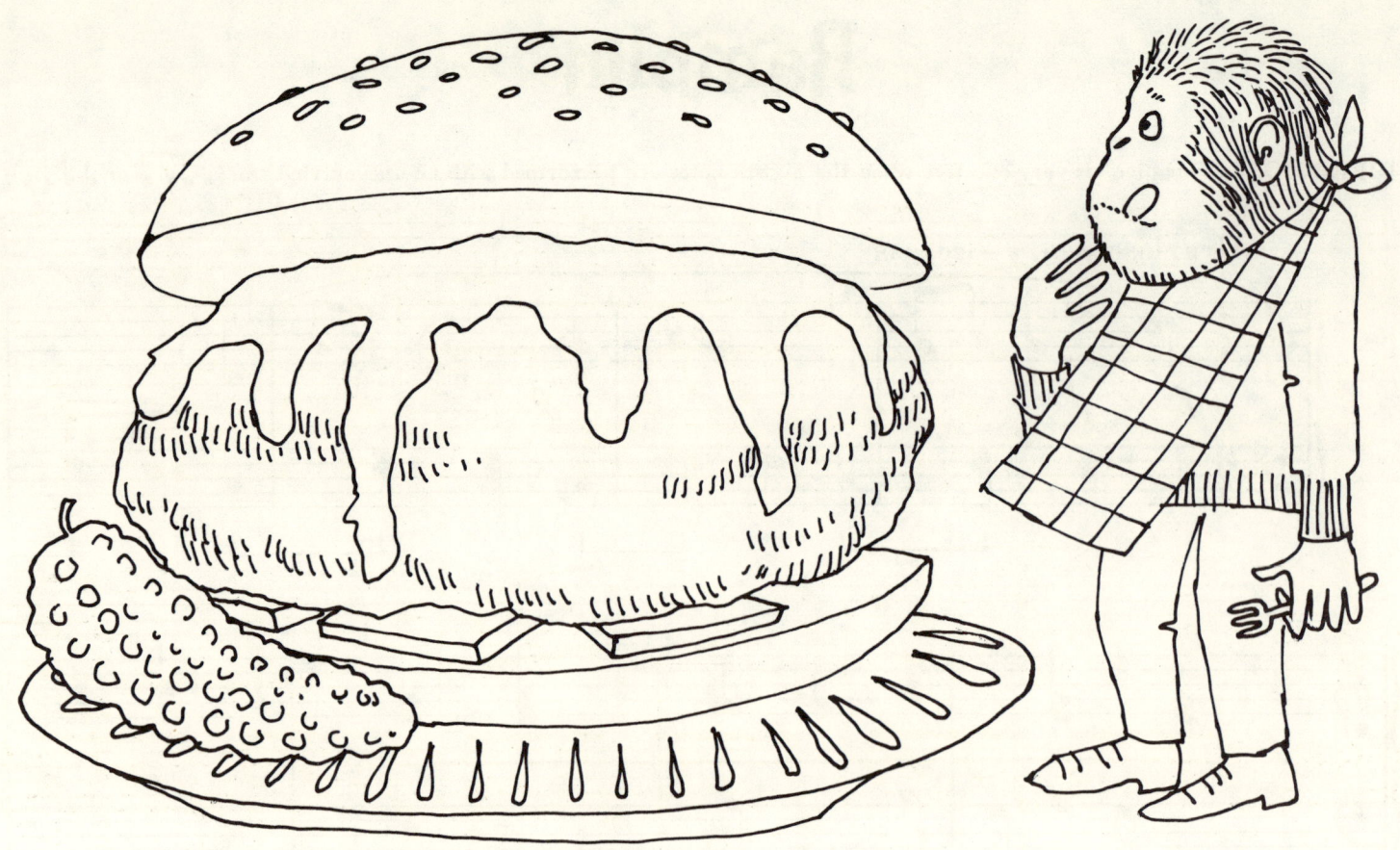

Giant Burger Blues

DIRECTIONS: This piece is very effective when the eighth notes are performed with an uneven rhythm.

Doloroso M.M. ♩=96–108

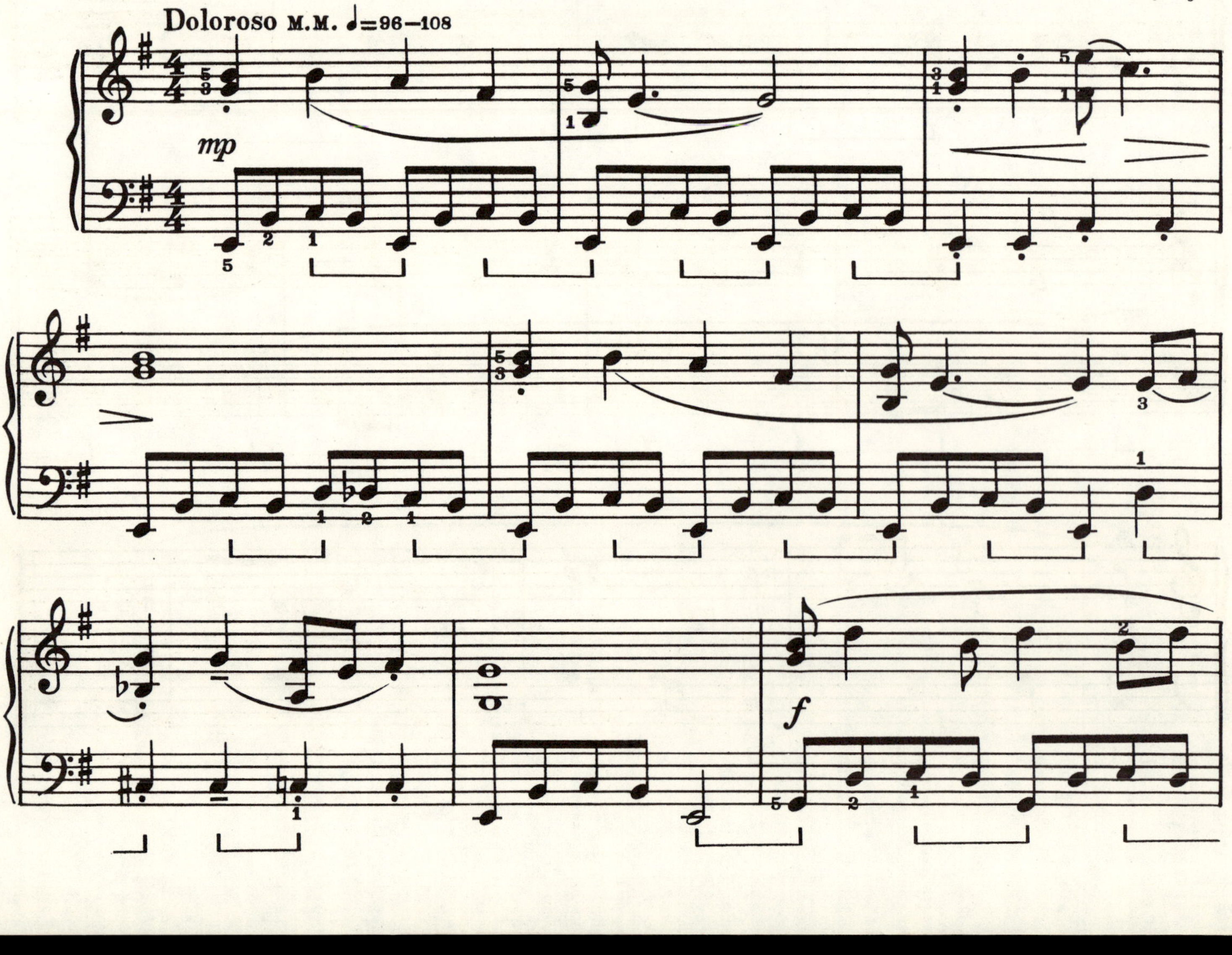

Think Young

The Elephant Twist

Rollin' Rhythm

She-Won't-Listen Blues

DIRECTIONS: This piece is very effective when the eighth notes are performed with an uneven rhythm:

Get Smart

Get Up and Go-Go

DIRECTIONS: This piece is very effective when the eighth notes are performed with an uneven rhythm.

Chip Dip

DIRECTIONS: This piece is very effective when the eighth notes are performed with an uneven rhythm:

27 FLAVORS

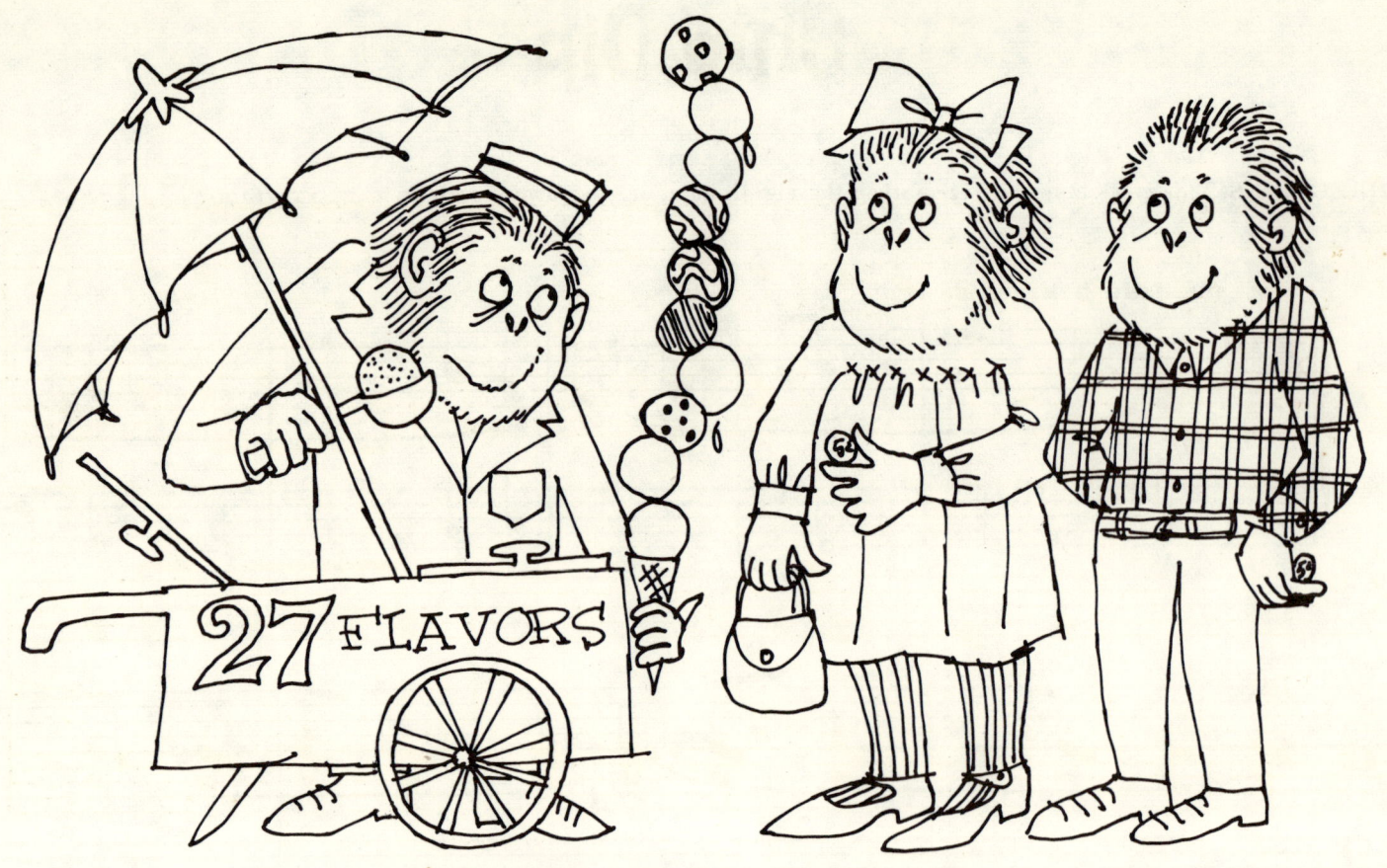

27 Flavors Blues

DIRECTIONS: This piece is very effective when the eighth notes are performed with an uneven rhythm:

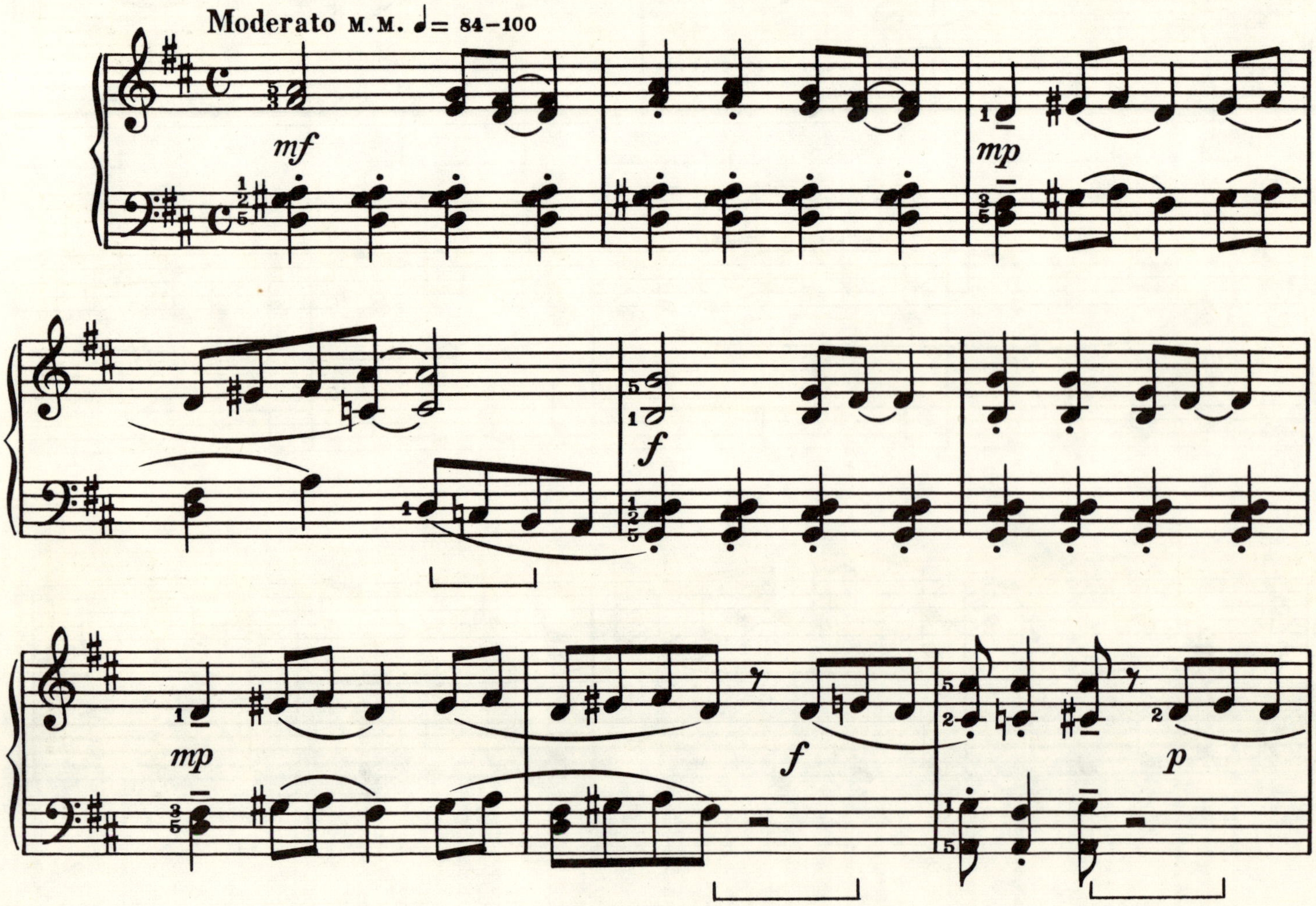
Moderato M.M. ♩= 84–100
mf
mp
f
mp
f
p

Runaround

DIRECTIONS: This piece is very effective when the eighth notes are performed with an uneven rhythm:

Juke Box Blues

DIRECTIONS: This piece is very effective when the eighth notes are performed with an uneven rhythm:

Big Blast

Graded List of Schaum Sheet Music
This is a Partial List — Showing Grade 2 thru Grade 4½ Titles

GRADE 2 – (C)

Armadillo Polka	John W. Schaum
Beach Ball Boogie	John W. Schaum
Candy Man	Bricusse & Newley
Country Rock	John Paul Jones
Dixie	Daniel D. Emmett
Fascination Waltz	F. D. Marchetti
Give My Regards to Broadway	Geo. M. Cohan
Harmony	Kaplan & Simon
Hava Nagila	Israeli Folk Dance
I'm An Old Cowhand	Johnny Mercer
In the Mood	Joe Garland
Joy Prelude	J. S. Bach
Let It Snow! Let It Snow! Let It Snow!	Jule Styne
Lift Ev'ry Voice and Sing	J. Rosamond Johnson
Matchmaker	Jerry Bock
National Emblem March	E. E. Bagley
Only You	Buck Ram & Ande Rand
Pollution Solution	John W. Schaum
Red Sails in the Sunset	Hugh Williams
Road Runner	John W. Schaum
Scarecrow Waltz	Patricia Craig
Send In the Clowns	Stephen Sondheim
Side by Side	Harry Woods
Sing, Robin Sing	Geo. L. Spaulding
Skate Board	Wesley Schaum
Ski Slope	Phyllis Warfel
Sleepy Lagoon	Eric Coates
South of the Border	Kennedy & Carr
Star-Spangled Banner	Commemorative Edition
Symphony No. 40 (First Theme)	W. A. Mozart
Texas Mother's Lullaby	May Foreman Carr
Yankee Doodle Dandy	Geo. M. Cohan
You're a Grand Old Flag	Geo. M. Cohan

GRADE 2½ – (D)

Beethoven's Fifth Symphony	1st Mvt. Theme
Birthday Bouquet (Piano SOLO)	(Theme & Variations)
Caravan	Rachel Beatty Kahl
Entertainer (Piano SOLO)	Scott Joplin
Fiddler on the Roof	Jerry Bock
Funeral March of a Marionette	Gounod
Fur Elise	Beethoven
I Believe	Drake, Graham, Shirl & Stillman
Marshmallow World	Peter DeRose
Melody in F	Anton Rubinstein
Minuet Medley	Bach
Moment Musical	Schubert
Mountain Majesty	Willa Waid Newman

GRADE 2½ – (continued)

On the Sunny Side of the Street	Jimmy McHugh
Santa's On His Way	John W. Schaum
Second Hand Rose	James F. Hanley
Shark Hunt	Edward J. Plank
Sonata in C	Mozart
Turkish March	Mozart
Yankee Doodle	(Theme & Variations)

GRADE 3 – (E)

Blue Danube	Johann Strauss, Jr.
Candy Cane Lane	Agnes D. Kastler
Corsage Waltz	John W. Schaum
Cotton Pickin' Boogie	Wm. H. Myddleton
Danse Macabre	Saint-Saens
Etude in E Major	Chopin
Hallelujah Chorus	Handel
Hawaiian Nocturne	Ladonna Weston
Neapolitan Serenade	Enrico Toselli
On Wings of Fantasy	Bea Lewis
Rustle of Spring	Sinding
Valse Triste	Sibelius

GRADE 4 – (F)

Ave Maria	Schubert
Christmas Fantasy	Moore-Schaum
Clair de Lune	Debussy
Forgotten Waltz	Liszt
Greensleeves	Cameo Transcription
Jingle Bells Jubilee	Concert Transcription
Journey To Bethlehem	Cecelia D. Williams
Kiss Me Again	Victor Herbert
La Danza	Rossini
Lento	Cyril Scott
March of the Toys	Victor Herbert
Solfeggietto	C. P. E. Bach
Toyland	Victor Herbert
Whistler and his Dog	Arthur Pryor

GRADE 4½ – (G)

After Theater Tango	Zez Confrey
Humoresque	Dvorak—Concert Transcription
Lotus Land	Cyril Scott
Mexican Hat Dance	Concert Transcription
Symphonic Rhapsody	Franck

PIANO DUETS – (1 Piano, 4 Hands)

Birthday Bouquet (Theme & Variations)	(2½)
Entertainer (Scott Joplin)	(2½)
Parade of the Toy Soldiers (Jessel)	(1)

Schaum Publications, Inc., Milwaukee, Wis. 53202